Trailblazers

Bugs and Spiders
by David Orme
Educational consultant: Helen Bird

Illustrated by Jorge Mongiovi

Published by Ransom Publishing Ltd.
51 Southgate Street, Winchester, Hants. SO23 9EH
www.ransom.co.uk

ISBN   978 184167 806 1

First published in 2009

Copyright © 2009 Ransom Publishing Ltd.

Illustrations copyright © 2009 Jorge Mongiovi
'Get the Facts' section - images copyright: stick insect Phobaeticus serratipes - Drägü; elephant - Kok Jynn Tan; insects - Robertas P?žas; American roach - Marcus Jones; millipede - Paul Marek; flea - Oliver Sun Kim; dust mite - U.S. Food and Drug Administration; louse - Centers for Disease Control and Prevention, U.S. Department of Health and Human Services; 3D rendered mite - Sebastian Kaulitzki; army ants - Mehmet Karatay; Tsetse fly - Geoffrey Attardo; mosquito - U.S. Department of Agriculture; Japanese hornet - Gary Alpert; honey bee - John Severns; locust - Michael Palis; dragonfly fossil - Amanda Rohde; ladybird - Tomasz Pietryszek; maggots - Dalius Baranauskas; Giant African millipede - Denis Ananiadis.

A CIP catalogue record of this book is available from the British Library.

Bugs and Spiders

Contents

Bugs and Spiders

Get the facts

Why are bugs amazing?

Scientists have found:

over a **million different insects** (though there are probably up to nine million more that they haven't found yet).

over **40,000 different types of spider** (though that's probably less than a quarter of the ones that exist).

They are the **most successful** of all the types of creature living on the Earth.

How come?

They can live in many places (**habitats**).

They live short lives.

They breed quickly.

This means that they can produce **huge numbers** of themselves.

Fruit fly
Can lay up to 800 eggs every day.
Ready to start breeding after two weeks.

Elephant
Usually has one calf every five years.
Ready to start breeding after 10 – 12 years.

Bug records

Biggest
Giant Walking Stick Insect. Up to 55 centimetres long!

Smallest
Fairy fly. Less than one fifth of a millimetre long!

Fastest runner
Tabanid fly – 145 kph!

Heaviest
Goliath beetle – 100 grams!

Fastest flier
Cockroach – 5 kph!

Most legs
Insects have 6 legs. But some **millipedes** have around 750 legs.

7

Spiders

Spider silk is amazing stuff. It is stronger than steel, but amazingly light.

400 kilometres of spider silk would weigh less than 5 grams!

Spiders are smart. They can make different sorts of silk for different jobs:

 Extra-strong silk to hold webs in place.

 Stickier silk for catching and wrapping up insects.

 Very light silk to act like a parachute.

The Weird Fact box:

In 1973 two spiders called Anita and Arabella were taken into space to see if they could spin webs in zero gravity.

Could they?

Yes – *after a bit of practice.*

Killer spiders

Only around 250 types of spider are dangerous to people.

These are the two most poisonous spiders:

Funnel Web spider

Brazilian Wandering spider

How deadly?

The Funnel Web spider is found in Australia. People who are bitten are given anti-venom. Even without the anti-venom, over 90% of people who are bitten do not die.

The Brazilian wandering spider is found in Central and South America. Some types hide in houses. They may bite if they are disturbed. Their venom is the most deadly of any spider.

So will their bite kill you?

Not usually. But it hurts a lot!

Human bugs – the yuk! page

Small creatures need places that are warm, safe, and have plenty of stuff to eat. A great place is the **human body**.

People think that because we are **much cleaner** now, we don't have bugs crawling over us.

Don't be so sure.

The flea

Human fleas aren't found on many people now. But they also live on **pigs**.

So if you shake hands with a friendly pig – watch out!

Body lice

Body lice lurk in your clothes. Then, when you are not expecting it – they start to **suck your blood**. They love blood so much that their bodies **swell up** until they **almost burst!**

Washing clothes – and us – means body lice are rare now.

But don't relax. What's that creeping around your head? It's ...

Head lice

It doesn't matter whether your hair is dirty or clean – head lice just love to be there, **drinking blood** from your scalp!

They inject spit into you to stop the blood clotting. Then they tuck in to a **delicious meal**!

Bed mites

Don't know them? Well, they know you! There are probably around three million of them lurking in your mattress.

They just love the **little flakes of skin** that fall off you all the time – delicious!

Most dangerous

This is the Giant Japanese Hornet – it is three inches long.

It kills about 70 people a year. Its sting is like 'a red hot nail being driven into you.'

But the Japanese get their own back – they eat them!

These are African Army ants on the march. They can kill and eat animals as big as pigs or goats – so don't hang around!

But these two are not the most deadly.

The **deadliest bugs** are those that spread disease.

This tsetse fly causes sleeping sickness in people and other diseases in animals. Unless it is treated straight away, sleeping sickness is fatal.

The **flea** can spread **bubonic plague** to humans. In the past, plagues wiped out at least a third of the population of the world.

So what's the deadliest bug of all?

This one. Mosquitoes spread a disease called **malaria**. It kills around a **million people** every year.

It is definitely the world's most dangerous bug.

Useful bugs

If it wasn't for bugs the world would be full of ... bugs.

WHY? Because bugs eat bugs!

The bugs people really hate are the ones that damage crops by eating them.

The **friendly bugs** are the ones that eat the plant-eating bugs, like this **ladybird**. These are called **predators**.

People spray **chemicals** that kill the bugs that eat crops.

Ladybirds are predators.

They like to eat greenfly for lunch.

BUT –

chemicals can kill the predators as well.

It can make things **worse**.

Some insects – like **bees** – are important because they spread **pollen** from one plant to another.

Some of these are in danger of disappearing.

WHY?

The **chemicals** can kill them too. And **climate change** may make life difficult for them.

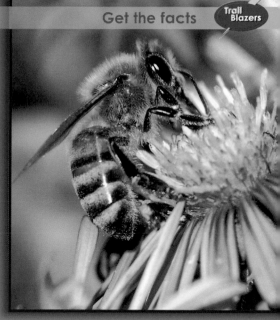

Tasty!

Here's another great use for bugs
— **eat them!**

Bugs make really **healthy food**, and if you cook them well, they're really crunchy!

Real bug recipes

Mealworms – Stir-fry them and serve with rice. Yummy!

Grasshopper chocolates – Bite into them for a big surprise!

Banana and maggot bread – First, wash and clean the maggots ...

Stop! I don't want to know!

Giant bugs

Why are bugs small? Why aren't there any **giant bugs**?

It's all to do with the way they breathe.

Mammals have lungs for breathing. Bugs breathe through **small holes** all over their bodies. These holes go to small tubes that do the job of lungs.

The trouble is, giant bugs would need really huge breathing tubes, and there wouldn't be room in their bodies.

The goliath beetle is as big as a bug can get.

I'm just having a breather.

16

Ancient bugs

Weren't there giant bugs around **millions of years ago**?

Dragonfly fossils have been found that are as big as large birds today.

Millipedes could be as long as a person.

In 2007 the **fossil claw** of a **giant sea scorpion** was found in Germany.

The animal it came from would have been over **2.5 metres long**!

But I thought that bugs can't grow that big.

They can't. But millions of years ago, there was **more oxygen** in the air than there is now.

Bugs' breathing tubes could **work better**.

So, maybe on an **alien planet** somewhere, where there is more oxygen in the air ...

17

What's Bugging You?

Chapter 1:
On an alien planet, somewhere ...

'There's certainly plenty of life on this planet!'

The space exploration team looked at the planet. It was a mass of green and blue.

'Any sign of intelligent life?'

'No radio or TV broadcasts. And I haven't spotted any cities.'

The ship went lower.

'This planet is very high in oxygen. We'd better wear helmets.'

Just then, the Navigator spotted something.

'Hey, check this out! What's that?'

Something that looked like a small, round hill was poking up through the jungle trees.

'That doesn't look natural,' said the chief scientist. 'Maybe there *is* life on this planet after all.'

'There's another one. And another! Those hills are everywhere! There's something going on here!'

'Looks interesting,' said the captain. 'Let's explore.'

Chapter 2:
Not friendly!

The navigator found a clearing in the forest near one of the strange hills.

The chief scientist got ready to go out. He took the ship's cook with him to act as a guard. They both wore helmets. Too much oxygen would make them feel drunk!

They walked towards the hill.

'Hey, there's an opening!' said the cook. 'Is it a cave?'

'The walls look too smooth to be a cave. I don't think that's natural.'

Things started to happen. Quickly.

A brown head with two huge eyes stared at them from the opening. Then the rest of the creature was out and rushing at them.

'It's an ant! But it's bigger than a person!'

The scientist and the cook turned to run back to the space ship. Hundreds of the giant ants were pouring out of the opening. And they didn't look friendly.

Chapter 3:
The cook gets caught

The scientist reached the airlock just in time. But the cook had eaten too much of his own food. He was slow.

The crew watched helplessly from the airlock as one of the ants picked him up. They were sure that the ants would tear him to pieces.

Then something strange happened.

All the ants stopped at the same moment. For a second or two, they stood totally still. Then the ant that was holding the cook dropped him to the ground. The huge creatures turned round and started to scuttle back to their giant ant hill.

The captain jumped up and rushed over to the cook.

'Are you alright?'

But the cook didn't speak. Ignoring the captain, he got up and started rushing after the ants!

Chapter 4:
Being an ant

The captain grabbed the cook and hung on.

'What are you doing, you idiot?'

But the cook didn't reply. He struggled to get away. Then the crew started yelling. The giant ants had turned back and were rushing towards them!

The braver members of the crew rushed to help. They dragged the cook into the airlock just in time. The ants couldn't break into the tough craft. Within seconds, it was heading for space.

'So what's it like, being an ant?' said the chief scientist.

'It was weird! I wasn't me any more. I was one of them!'

'The minds of those ants were linked. That's why they do everything at the same time. Your brain picked up the signals.'

'So why didn't it happen to you?'

'You must have a very special brain, like an ant.' said the scientist.

The cook was pleased.

'What's special about an ant's brain, then?'

'It's a very small one!'

Bugs and Spiders word check

adapt	millipede
allergic	mosquito
anti-venom	oxygen
bubonic plague	parachute
chemicals	poisonous
climate change	pollen
clotting	predator
deadly	sleeping sickness
fatal	tsetse fly
habitat	venom
malaria	zero gravity